NEEM

Uses & Medicinal Propert

GW00771463

Dr. Rajeev Sharma

MANOJ PUBLICATIONS

ISBN : 978-81-310-0741-9
Eighth Edition : 2016

Printers :
Jai Maya Offset
Jhilmil Industrial Area, Delhi-110095

Neem : Dr. Rajeev Sharma

PREFACE

The word 'neem' is derived form the Sanskrit *Nimba* which means to bestow health—which signifies the great therapeutic value of this plant. All parts of neem plant have medicinal properties and used extremely in Indian traditional systems of medicine. Neem oil is endowed with many medicinal properties and there are many neem oil based traditional preparations used for pesticides, fungicides and also for treating many human diseases.

The ancient Indians thus believed that neem is destroyer of all diseases and provide them with excellent health and prosperity including mosquito repellent. Perhaps of this strong faith in neem promoted them to plant neem in the courtyard of houses, in public places and on road sides. It is also custom in India to spread neem leaves on around the bed of the chicken pox patients and after recovery the patients are given their first bath in a water which is preboiled with neem leaves. It is believed that this will prevent from spreading the chicken pox and also hasten the healing of the pox marks and also protect the skin.

In this book the subject is covered to its full. We try our best to cover every aspect of neem, its medicinal and industrial use along with home remedies.

—Publishers

CONTENTS

NEEM – INTRODUCTION

Botanical name : Azadirachta Indica

Common names : Neem, nim, Indian lilac, nimmi, limbo, limda.

Neem is a native tree of India, a tropical tree especially suited to semi-arid conditions. It is now grown in many Asian countries and in the tropical regions of the western hemisphere. Neem is considered to be part of India's genetic bio-diversity. It is a medium large tree having short, straight bole, furrowed, dark brown to gray bark, and dense rounded crown of pinnate leaves.

Native to India and other south Asia countries, Neem is widely planted and naturalized in semi-arid areas throughout Asia and Africa.

Unique Properties

Neem is an evergreen tree of the tropics and sub-tropics. It belongs to the family Meliaceae and is becoming increasingly popular for its insect repellant traits and unique property of inhibiting the nitrification process in the soil. In India, Neem grows in the plains and in areas up to an elevation of 1850 m. In its introduced range, Neem is cultivated from sea level to an altitude of 1500 m. Neem is tolerant to most soil types including dry, stony, shallow soils, lateritic crusts, highly leached sands and clays.

With an extensive and deep root system, the hardy Neem can grow and flourish even in marginal and leached soils. The Neem tree flowers between February and May.

The honey-scented white flowers, found in clusters are a good source of nectar for bees. Neem fruits are green drupes which turn golden yellow on ripening in the month of June, July and August in India.

The termite resistant neem timber is used as a building material and in making furniture and farm implements. The bark yields tannin and gum. The amber-hued gum is

used as a dye in textiles and traditional medicines. Leaves are used as fodder and green manure. Neem derivatives such as Azadirachtin, nimbicidin and a host of other compounds are now used in medicines and commercial pesticides. Many bioactive ingredients have been identified and isolated, the most important ones being azadirachtin and meliantriol.

The most active, currently identified ingredient of Neem is 'Azadirachtin'. It finds applications in Neem-based pesticide formulations which are safe, natural, bio-degradable, manageable at the farmer's level and environment friendly, unlike chemical and synthetic pesticides which leave behind residues polluting air, water and soil.

Neem Rasayana

Neem, also known as nimba or margosa, is regarded by the ancients and modern science alike as a powerful healing herb with diverse applications. Described in the Ayurvedic texts as *sarva roga nivarini*—that which keeps all diseases at bay or *arishtha*, reliever of disease. Neem has been used in the Ayurvedic tradition for thousands of years to maintain health. The roots, bark, gum, leaves, fruit, seed kernels and seed oil are all used in therapeutic preparations for both internal and topical use.

☐☐

NEEM TREE COMPONENTS

Since ancient times, neem has been associated with healing in the sub-continent of India. A large number of medicinals, cosmetics, toiletries and pharmaceuticals are now based on neem derivatives because of it's unique properties.

Bark : Neem bark is cool, bitter, astringent, acrid and refrigerant. It is useful in tiredness, cough, fever, loss of appetite, worm infestation. It heals the wounds and is also used in vomiting, skin diseases and excessive thirst.

Leaves : According to Ayurveda, neem leaves help in the treatment of *vatik* disorders (neuro muscular pains). Neem leaves are also reported to remove toxins, purify blood and prevent damage caused by free radical in the body by neutralising them. Neem leaves are reported to be beneficial in eye disorders and insect bite poisons.

Fruits : Neem fruits are bitter, purgative, antihemorrhodial and anthelmintic in nature.

Flowers : Neem flowers are used in vitiated conditions of *pitta* (balancing of the body heat) and *kapha* (cough formation). They are astringent, anthelmintic and non-toxic.

Seeds : Neem seeds are also described as anthelmintic, antileprotic, antipoisonous and bitter in taste.

Oil : Neem oil derived from crushing the seeds is antidermatonic, a powerful anthelmintic and is bitter in taste. It has a wide spectrum of action and is highly medicinal in nature.

Mixture : Five parts of Neem tree *i.e.* Bark, Root, Fruit, Flower and Leaves together are used in diseases of blood. It is also used in vitiated conditions of excess heat, itching, wound, burning sensation in body and skin diseases.

❑❑

NEEM HERB—SYSTEM PURIFIER

Neem is a large, evergreen tree and has strong health maintaining properties. It has been used as a tonic and astringent that promotes wound healing. Neem's traditional use is based on its detoxifying benefits that help maintain healthy circulatory, digestive, respiratory and urinary systems. It is used for external applications in skin diseases. Neem extracts possess antidiabetic, antibacterial, and antiviral properties. Its principle constituents are nimbin, nimbinin and nimbidin. All parts of the plant yield b-sitosterol.

All the parts of the plant and active principles and extracts possess a lot of significant pharmacological properties. Neem is bitter and alterative. It is used as a poultice in boils, is antiseptic, demulcent, a tonic in catarrhal affections, stomachic, stimulant. It is useful in snake bite, scorpion sting, hypoglycemic, in rheumatism, as an analgesic, antipyretic, sedative, antibacterial, antiprotozoal, antiviral, anthelmintic and in skin diseases. The tree stem, root and bark possess astringent, tonic, and antiperiodic properties. The bark is beneficial in malarial fever and useful in cutaneous diseases.

One of the most powerful blood purifiers and detoxifiers in Ayurvedic usage, Neem is often used to maintain healthy skin. There is plenty of scientific backup for Neem's immune enhancement properties as a booster of the macrophage's effectiveness. Scientific studies indicate that Neem boosts the immune system by energizing lymphocytes cells to respond to infection and other challenges to the body's immunity. Clinical trials were conducted on 9 patients of congestive heart failure with anasarca to study the diuretic effect of sodium nimbidinate. 250mg were administered daily by deep intra-muscular injection in the gluteal region. The injections were repeated for 2-13 days with an average of about 5 injections per patient. Four other patients were also studied as controls on the same lines with bed rest, low sodium diet and adequate digitalization without any diuretic. Eight of the patients showed a definite diuretic response. The control group did not show any diuresis. No toxic reaction was noted except local discomfort or slight pain. Clinical trials were conducted on 12 cases of congestive cardiac failure with sodium nimbidinate for diuretic activity. Encouraging diuretic activity was observed with good response in 4 cases. There was no significant toxicity.

⬛⬜

NEEM USES & BENEFITS

Neem needs no introduction in today's world. A very famous herb of India with worldwide fame and having magical properties known for its miraculous medicinal values from past 5000 years. Neem is known as free tree of India as it is found almost everywhere in India. It is considered as a magic tree, which has properties that not only relieves but also cures from illness. Neem tree is commonly known as Margosa tree in English language and Azadirachta Indica in biological terms. It is part of every Indian home due to its great application and hence is considered as a place of worship.

Margosa tree attains a maximum height of 40 to 50 fts. It is an evergreen tree whose branches spread all over. It is a very densely crowned tree, which may reach to a diameter of 30 to 40 fts. The trunk is relatively straight. Bark is thick and rough with whitish to reddish brown in appearance. A fluid called *neera* excrudes out of the bark. Leaves are pinnate 12 to 15 inch long with about 20 to 31 green coloured leaflets, which are about 3 to 5 cm in length. Flowers are small and white in colour that blossom in spring *i.e.* February to March. Fruits are oval in appearance green in colour, when in raw form and turns pale yellow when it ripes. Every fruit contains one seed, which contain oil. Neem tree fruits in summers *i.e.* in May to July. Neem has been used as pesticide since early ages because of its remarkable property of fighting away with pest and microorganism, that are supposed to be harmful for agricultural and homely purpose and hence makes neem the most wonderful partner of human in his evolution.

Margosa tree possesses the *sheet* (cold) *virya* potency. It contains *tickta* and *kashaya rasa*, it possesses the *laghu* (light) *gunna* (property). Combination of these makes neem a unique herb. Due to *tickta rasa* it suppresses *kapha* and due to *sheet virya* potency it suppresses *pitta dosha*. Chemically neem contains complex compounds called triterpenes, limonoids, nonterpenoids, hexanortriterpenoids, and pentattriterpenoids. The most important active ingredient of neem is azadirachitin, which makes neem possess the power, what it projects in its usage. Every part of the plant is used *i.e.* flower, leaves, bark, seed, oil, branches and the excludant called *neera*, which flows out of the bark.

Neem is a multipurpose herb, which is recommended in every type of ailment. Following are the wonders of neem, which ayurveda has to offer to this world and modern life style of living.

Local Action

❐ Neem act as anti bacterial, anti parasitic, anti fungal, anti protozoal and anti viral thus helps in protection from all the microorganisms, which are always ready to invade in our body causing serious ailments.

❐ Local application of neem powder or neem oil has miraculous results. As it is a famous anti microbial herb, it renders all the microorganisms inactive therefore helping in proper healing of wound without causing any infections and septic conditions.

❐ Taking bath of neem leaves water is a very common sight in Indian homes that helps our body to counter mild infections, which our body might get in day-to-day activity.

❐ Its tropical application makes us relieved from acne, eczema and even ringworms.

❐ In skin related diseases, neem works as blessing of God on mankind. It has an action on almost every kind of skin disease thus making its indication in eradicating every kind of itch, rash, infection and allergy.

☐ Neem water is extensively used in burn injuries, thus to protect them from any kind of infection and also promote healing.

☐ Neem oil is extensively used in hair fall and early graying of hairs with very satisfying results. It also find its application in dandruff and in lice growth.

☐ Its local application on arthritic conditions like rheumatoid arthritis, gout, Osteoarthritis, lower back pain, and musculo skeletal pains is highly recommended with good results.

Internal Action

☐ Due to presence of *tickta rasa* it is beneficial in indigestion, constipation and restoring taste of mouth.

☐ It helps in fighting with the intestinal worms there by act as a deworming agent.

☐ It is highly recommended in hyperacidity and epigastric pain as it suppresses pitta that is the main culprit in the aggravation of such illness.

☐ Good results have also been seen in gastritis.

☐ Widely and extensively used as blood purifier as it possess the properties like *tickta rasa* which helps in detoxifying any toxins floating in our blood stream which may lead to illness.

☐ It gives wonderful results in diabetes incipidus and diabetes mellitus due to presence of *tickta rasa*.

☐ It is very helpful in curing urinary tract infection.

☐ It stimulates liver for proper functioning therefore helps in maintaining proper secretions of liver.

☐ It acts on all kinds of skin disorders and provides great relief.

- It works as an anti inflammatory and pain relieving agent.

- It also helps in suppressing extra heat generated in body due to any reason thus helps in maintaing normal condition in hyperthermia. Very useful in suppressing fever.

- Anti malarial action of neem has also been seen.

- Since old times neem leaves have been used as an agent that helps in increasing vision as it helps in suppressing kapha disorders thus releasing congestion on eyeballs caused due to mucus accumulation in sinuses.

- Coughing is relieved by use of neem water.

- It helps in reducing excess micturation.

- It has given very good results in diseases like gonorrhea and syphilis.

- It works as an immune boosting agent therefore making our immune system very strong and efficient to fight against any foreign invasion making our body strong and disease free.

NEEM LEAVES

Neem leaves are widely used to cure a number of human and animal diseases. The physio-chemical properties of neem leaves help to maintain the overall well being. Leaves are also used to manufacture a number of drugs and medicines. They have been traditionally used to give bath to patients suffering from measles or chicken pox.

Neem leaves are generally gathered only from organic trees, this is so, because it ensures the protection of natural elements and reduction of contamination by environmental/synthetic toxins.

Neem leaves can be taken as following—

❐ Raw Leaves

❐ Neem Leaf Extract

❐ Neem Leaf Juice

Neem Leaves Processing

❐ Mature green leaves are collected and allowed to dry partially in shade and are then crushed into powder.

❐ Powdered leaves are then soaked, normally overnight in water (for aqueous extraction) or in organic solvents (for organic extraction); the extract is strained through a cloth the next morning. Aqueous extract is rich in carbohydrates, pigments, water soluble amino acids.

❐ The extract can then be used for desired purpose.

Uses of Neem Leaves in Industries : Neem leaves are extensively used in a number of industries, leaves are either used in the raw form, extracts or in powdered form and is an important ingredient/composition in a number of products.

Pharmaceutical Industry : Neem leaves find a number of uses to prevent, cure and treat a number of diseases and ailments. A large number of drugs and herbal medicines have neem leaves as their active ingredient.

Skin Care Products : Used as a potent cure for acne, pimples, blemishes. A large number of herbal product manufacturers make extensive use of neem leaves to make medicated herbal facial creams, lotions, syrups for dermatological problems.

Many drug manufacturers make use of neem leaves for producing important drugs meant for diabetes, blood pressure, psoriasis, malaria, ulcer etc make use of neem leaves as an important composition/ingredient.

Cosmetic Industry : With the increasing popularity of herbs and herbal products, leading manufacturers are using neem leaves in a number of creams, lotions, hair care products such as hair oils, conditioners, hair rejuvenating tonics etc.

Agricultural Industry : Neem leaves are of tremendous use in agricultural industry; the leaves possess insect repellent properties and are used as herbal pesticides, insecticides. Azadirachtin is the principle ingredient used in the manufacture of fertilizers and manure.

Herbal Industry : Neem leaf is an important ingredient used in a number of herbal products, right from skin care to hair care, from oral care to herbal cosmetics. Leaves are used in ayurvedic and unani medicines.

NEEM LEAF EXTRACT

Neem leaf extract has a fruit like smell and contains

essential fatty acids; this extract finds large scale personal and industrial application. They are used in a number of pesticides and insecticides, high potency extracts are used to manufacture personal products like facial creams, skin creams, cleansers and oral care products.

Process of Neem Leaf Extraction

❑ Mature green leaves are collected and allowed to dry partially.

❑ These dried leaves are then crushed and powdered.

❑ The crushed leaves are then subjected to either aqueous or organic solvent to get a concentrated extract.

Certain extraction process utilizes carbon dioxide at critical temperatures and pressures to extract the active ingredients of the neem leaf, the usual high temperatures or harsh chemicals are done away with, resulting in a better concentrated and potent extract.

Use of Neem Leaf Extract

Medicine : It is extensively used as a cure for inflammation and number of skin related diseases like acne, rashes, blemishes, maturing of skin etc.

Agriculture : Used to manufacture natural and organic pesticides and insecticides, can be used as an anti feedant and helps in the growth and promotion of plants.

Cosmetics : Used to manufacture face and body creams in the personal hygiene industry.

Oral Care : Leaf extracts have been used widely in both traditional and current times to manufacture tooth pastes and mouthwash in the oral care industry. Its anti bacterial properties helps to keep dental problems at bay.

❏❏

NEEM SEEDS & KERNELS

Neem seeds are one of the most useful part of the tree, finding use in different industries to make range of products. It has the maximum number of compounds with curative properties. It is used to manufacture effective pesticides as seeds have the highest content of azadirachtin.

Raw Neem Seed : Raw neem seed can also be used in powdered form as a soil conditioner and promoting the growth of plants.

Neem Seed Extract : Used in agriculture, medicines, oral care, ayurveda and unani system of medicine.

Neem Seed Oil : It possesses medicinal properties and is used for large number of diseases. Used in pharmaceuticals, cosmetics, agriculture, veterinary diseases.

Neem Seed Processing

Cleaning : Foreign material and impurities like dirt, stones, sticks, stems etc have to be removed by means of screen-air-separator and destoner. There are machines that separate light, oversize and undersize impurities.

Depulping : Fruits are soaked in water for a few days which helps to remove the skin and get the seed, they are then dried which can in turn be of tray or rotatory type. Thereafter seeds or fruits are dehulled into impact hullers.

Extraction: Seeds are then be treated with water based and organic solvents to make concentrated extracts.

Use of Neem Seed

Neem seed is used for livestock production as it has a very high nutritional value, it has large quantities of protein, which makes it all the more valuable. It can however not be used for food because of its bitter taste and foul odour. Compounds containing sulphur such as nimbidin, nimbosterol are responsible for the bitter taste of seeds and a principle, tignic acid is the cause of foul smell of seeds; they also have high insecticidal properties.

Neem seed in the raw and extracts form is also used to manufacture facial creams, body lotions and other cosmetics seeds are also highly useful in preparing drugs and medicines both in traditional system such as ayurveda as well as modern allopathic drugs.

Neem seeds are also widely used by farmers and agriculturists as a natural pesticide and insecticide, neem extracts inhibit the growth of insects by altering their life cycle.

Neem seeds are also used in hair care products right from shampoo to hair lotions etc.

NEEM KERNEL

Kernel is the inner part of the neem seed, it is generally soft. It is the richest source of neem oil and is used widely in agriculture. They are dehulled and grinded for extraction. Kernels can either be aqueously extracted or with a solvent depending on which active compound is required.

Forms of Neem Kernel

❏ Raw Kernel   ❏ Kernel Extracts

❏ Kernel Powder   ❏ Kernel Oil

Benefits of Neem Kernel

❏ Used in preparation of pesticides, insecticides and manure.

❏ Can be used with neem cake and has anti feedant properties.

❏ Used in crop and plant protection.

❏ Used to manufacture skin products.

❏ Used in ayurvedic medicines.

❏ Used to protect cattle from ticks and lice.

❑❑

NEEM FRUITS & GUMS

Neem fruit is green in colour initially and gradually turns to yellow when fully ripened. A matured fruit is very fleshy and filled with sweetish fluid. Fruit contains 40-55% water content. Collection of fruits requires organized and planned plantation and collection efforts.

Types of Neem Fruit

For collection and storage purpose, neem fruits can be divided into four categories:

❏ Dry (upto10 % moisture)

❏ Semi-Dry (11-20% moisture)

❏ Fresh (about 50% moisture)

❏ Wet and damaged

Forms of Neem Fruit

❏ Raw fruit

❏ Powdered fruit

❏ Fruit extract

❏ Neem fruit juice

Neem Fruit Processing

❏ Cleaning

❏ Dehulling

❏ Solvent Extraction

❏ Depulping

❏ Grinding

Use of Neem Fruit in Industries

Pharmaceutical Industry : Neem fruit, pulp and extracts are used to manufacture medicines and drugs curing diseases like diabetes, leprosy, skin disorders, constipation etc.

Cosmetic Industry : Powdered form or extracts of fruits are used to manufacture herbal shampoos, soaps, creams and ointments.

Agriculture Industry : Compounds present in neem fruits possess pest and insect repellent properties, therefore it is used on a large scale to manufacture bio and natural insecticides and pesticides.

Veterinary Use : seeds are said to be used for wildlife food. It is relatively non toxic to animals.

NEEM GUM

Gum is a by product obtained as a result of certain metabolic mechanism of plants and trees. The Neem bark, due to some internal activity discharges a clear, bright and brown-coloured gum. The gum is a multipurpose by product. Natural gum obtained from plants are either water soluble or absorb water to form a viscous solution. Neem has been commercially tapped for using its gum which is of use in large number of industries. It is being grown on a large scale basis for using all its parts, no wonder it is called a 'Universal Tree' having a cure for almost everything. It has been used traditionally as a adhesive for paintings.

Use in Industries

Cosmetic Industry : Used in facial masks, lotions, face powder, protective creams.

Paper Industry : Used as an adhesive and strengthening the paper.

Pharmaceutical Industry : Used in antiseptic creams, tablet binder, and coater.

Textile Industry : Used in dyeing and printing of fabrics.

Personal Hygiene Industry : Used in soaps, tooth paste, tooth powders.

Food Industry : Used as a stabilizing agent, gels and thickening agent.

□□

NEEM BARK

Bark of the neem tree contains medicinal properties and is used in a number of industries. Neem bark has traditionally been used in a number of medicine systems like Ayurveda, Unani etc. It is used to manufacture a number of skin and personal hygiene products. It is a multi functional as well as multi utility natural product and without any side effects. The bark contains 3.43% protein, 0.68% alkaloids and 4.16% minerals. Polysaccharides in neem bark extracts is said to have possess anti-tumor as well as anti-inflammatory properties.

USE OF NEEM BARK IN INDUSTRIES

Neem bark finds varied uses in a number of industries. Manufacturers use it in either raw form or in extracts or powdered form to produce a number of products.

Herbal Industry

The medicinal properties of neem bark makes it a popular ingredient in a number of herbal medicines, herbal cosmetics. Neem bark is extensively used in preparation of Ayurveda and Unani system of traditional medicines. It is also used to manufacture herbal teas with curative properties.

Agricultural Industry

Neem bark has proved to be a boon for farmers. It finds immense use in agricultural industry; the bark possesses insect repellent properties and are used as herbal pesticides, insecticides etc. It helps to retard the growth of insects and pests.

Oral Care Industry

Neem bark is used as an active ingredient in a number of tooth pastes and tooth powders. This is so, because neem bark has anti bacterial properties, good for curing

gum problems and maintaining dental health naturally; Bark powder and extracts are used in treating fevers and stomach problems. Studies show that neem bark is more active than the leaves against certain bacteria.

Cosmetic Industry

Herbal cosmetics have become very popular in the last few years, this is because of the fact that men and women realise that herbs not only have therapeutic value but also do not have any side effects. Neem bark is used as extracts or powdered form in a number of herbal cosmetics. Acne treating and other skin creams used neem bark to cure pimples and improve the skin condition.

Tanning and Dyeing Industry

Neem bark contains tannin, so it is useful in tanning and dyeing a number of products.

□□

NEEM ROOTS & TWIGS

Neem roots are long, thick, penetrating and can go up to 20 meters. The tree can adapt to the extreme hot and humid climate because of the ability of its root system to extract water from deep down. A well established root system provides support and strength to the entire tree and is responsible for its growth.

Form of Neem Root

❒ Root Powder

❒ Root Extracts

❒ Raw Roots

Properties of Neem Root

❒ Antiseptic

❒ Anti bacterial

❒ Anti fungal

❒ Germicidal

Use of Neem Root

Medicine : Roots of neem tree are used to manufacture medicines and drugs for curing different ailments. It is used as an active ingredient in medicines meant for killing worms in human body. Also used to manufacture oils curing sinusitis.

Oral Hygiene : Roots are also used, in toothpastes and tooth powders as the antibacterial and germicidal properties helps to keep dental hygiene and prevent diseases, it also helps to strengthen the gums.

NEEM TWIGS

Neem twig has lots of pharmacological properties and is used to manufacture oral care products. It is used to manufacture herbal toothpastes and powders. It has found mention in the early vedic texts, for being of immense importance in maintaining oral hygiene. A neem twig is considered a very effective natural or herbal toothbrush, while its fibres clean the teeth, its juice works both as a mouth freshener and has germ-killing properties. It has also been used for a long time now, for manufacturing organic manure. They are being grown and exported to countries for meeting different uses.

Forms of Neem Twig

- Raw Twig
- Twig Oil
- Twig Extracts
- Twig Powder

Properties of Neem Twigs

- Anti Pyretic
- Anti fungal
- Antibacterial
- Germicidal

Use of Neem Twigs in Industries

Agriculture : Neem twig can be used to manufacture mulch and natural manure.

Oral Care : Neem twig extracts and powder are used to manufacture tooth pastes and tooth powders. It helps to strengthen and ward off gum diseases, keeps the teeth stronger and help prevent periodontal diseases.

❏❏

USES OF NEEM OIL

Apart from its previously described application for storage protection, neem oil has been a trusted remedy for a naturally healthy skin in the villages of India. Derived from the seeds of the neem tree it contains all the disinfecting and healing properties of the tree, in a concentrated easily usable form. For centuries, this therapeutic oil has provided protection and Scientific studies have shown that Neem contains certain chemicals, which are unique.

The primary chemicals are a mixture of 3-4 related compounds called limonoids. Neem seeds also contain a few chemicals that have sulphur. These phyto-chemicals add the characteristic smell to the neem oil. They also attach additional curative properties to the oil. It has a dark yellow colour, turns solid at temperatures below twenty-three degrees Celsius, and does not dry out. The oil is composed mainly of glycerides of palmitin, stearin, oil and linol acids. It chemically resembles soy oil or olive oil. In the cold-pressed oil, there are also 10 to 20 percent of the total content of biologically active components, especially the limonoids. Bitter components contained in neem oil and certain sulphur compounds that give the oil its strong garlic scent, destroy the taste.

It is a completely natural total first aid tool for families. Due to its unique composition it has an almost magical effect on chronic skin conditions that fail to respond to conventional treatments. What makes neem oil outstanding in comparison to other remedies is that it is active against all three varieties of infectious organisms: Bacteria, Fungii and Viruses. The oil is known to provide a very effective germicidal action. Modern science has now confirmed the effectiveness of neem oil in fighting infection. Scientific studies indicate that neem has very powerful skin rejuvenating qualities and it is being hailed as the *Oil of Wonder*.

Many strains of bacteria are found to be resistant to the modern antibiotics. Neem oil has a seemingly endless range of antibacterial uses. This has prompted the development of neem as an anti-bacterial drug for these resistant strains, against which it has shown promising activity in the laboratory tests. Because of its antiseptic qualities, neem oil is also well suited for medicinal soaps and pharmaceuticals such as salves and creams. Neem oil is used in cosmetics for creams, lotions and shampoos.

It has a wide spectrum of action and can be safely used for a variety of skin conditions. Neem oil and many of its constituents have been successfully used against a wide range of bacteria, viruses, fungi and parasites. Neem oil has been reported to be effective against certain human fungi, which are even difficult to control, by modern synthetic fungicides. These include some Trichophyton, Epidermophyton, Microsporum, Trichosporon, Geotricum and Candida. Neem oil inhibited the growth of all the three strains of Mycobacterium in a concentration of 12.5 mg/ml.

Neem oil absorbs quickly into the skin and has good skin penetration. It's compounds are non-irritating and are known to have a minimum of allergic reactions. It is neither too hot (*ushna*) nor too cold (*sheetha*) in potency (*veerya*) and subsides *pitta* and *kapha dosha*, promoting holistic health for mind, body and spirit.

If you are looking for a natural remedy for skin irritations, pure medicinal grade Neem oil could well be your answer.

□□

BEAMING HEALTH WITH NEEM

Neem grows in tropical and semi tropical regions and is widely found in Burma, India and Pakistan. This is a very fast growing, evergreen tree which reaches the height of 15 to 20 meters.

Neem is known for its immeasurable medicinal properties and is used as a main ingredient in many home remedies. Commending the medicinal properties of Neem, numerous Sanskrit names have been coined by our Ayurveda *acharyas*. Few of them are mentioned below :

☐ It is known as *Nimba* as it boosts health.

☐ It is praised as *Pichumarda* as it destroys skin diseases.

☐ As it is used to ward off evil powers that harm our body, it is known as *Arishta*.

Chemical composition of Neem

Neem tree has numerous medicinal properties by virtue of its chemical compounds. Seeds of the Neem tree contain the highest concentration of Azadirachtin. Apart from Azadirachtin, salannin, gedunin, azadirone, nimbin, nimbidine, nimbicidine, nimbinol, etc are other important liminoids of neem.

Uses of Neem in Horticulture

Neem has been the most traditionally used plant in India, Pakistan and Africa to protect grains and cereals from pests. Fresh neem leaves are mixed with grains and cereals before storing. A paste of fresh neem leaves is rubbed against the wall of large mud bins or gunny bags in which the grains and cereals are stored. Some times a thick layer of dry neem leaves are spread over grains. Neem oil extracted from seeds acts as best bio-pesticide. Jute sacks treated with neem oil or extracts of neem are used to store food grains. Neem oil is a very cheap and effective household pesticide to protect grains and legumes from pests. Neem is being used to protect stored roots and tubers from potato moth.

Azadirachtin is available in high concentration in neem seeds. It is used as 'botanical pesticide' which is environmentally friendly. It prevents insects from feeding on plants and regulates the growth of insects. Neem extracts do not harm the insects like bees, spiders and butterflies which help in pollination.

Medicinal Properties of Neem

The Neem tree has many medicinal uses. The chemical compounds present in Neem have anti-inflammatory, anti-arthritic, antipyretic, hypoglycaemic, anti-fungal, spermicidal, anti-malarial, anti-bacterial and diuretic properties. Flower, leaves, bark and seeds of Neem are used in home remedies and in preparation of medicines. Bark of Neem acts as antipyretic and helps to reduce fever. Flowers are used in intestinal disorders. Juice from fresh leaves is very helpful in treating skin diseases, wounds and obesity. Oil from neem seeds is used in arthritis, skin diseases and muscular sprains. Neem is very effective in treating gum diseases.

The neem is proved to be beneficial in treating skin diseases because of its antibiotic, antifungal and blood purifying properties. According to Ayurveda principles vitiated *kapha* and *pitta* cause skin diseases. Neem pacifies vitiated *kapha* and *pitta*, thus helps to cure skin ailments. It promotes wound healing as it is antibacterial and astringent. In psoriasis it reduces itching, irritation, roughness of skin and heals the psoriatic patches. In same way it heals eczema too. It reduces infection and inflammation of acne. Neem helps to maintain the health of scalp skin and prevents dandruff.

Due to its detoxifying properties it helps to keep organ systems healthy, especially circulatory, digestive, respiratory and urinary systems.

Scientific studies have revealed that neem reduces blood sugar level. Hence its usage supports diabetic patients to keep their blood sugar level in control. Diabetes impairs blood circulation and causes gangrene in lower extremities. Numerous scientific researches have highlighted the role of neem in keeping circulatory system healthy, thus reducing the chances of gangrene. Recent studies have shown that neem reduces blood cholesterol level and keeps the heart healthy.

Neem in Household

Neem flower pachidi is prepared from roasted neem flower and is a famous dish in South India which is prepared during Ugadi. Neem flower rasam improves digestion and is very popular in Andhra and Tamilnadu.

Extract of skin friendly neem is being used in manufacturing bathing soaps, hair gels etc.

□□

TIPS ON USING NEEM

The neem tree exemplifies Mahatma Gandhi's concept of economy of permanence and has much to offer in solving global, agricultural, environmental and public health problems. No other tree can match neem's usefulness. Neem rightfully belongs to the millions of ordinary Indians who learnt to put it to use, as it is this knowledge, passed down through generations, that has helped scientists discover neem's amazing potential. The commercial and industrial prospects of neem are unlimited and exciting. There is no other tree that touches the life and living of such a majority of the country's population.

❑ Mix pure dried neem oil with Vaseline in the ratio of 1:5. This combination can be used for repelling insects including mosquitoes as well as for skin disorders, minor cuts, burns, wounds etc.

❑ For complete skin protection make a strong tea with neem leaves and add to the bath along with a little rose water.

❑ Boil 10 freshly cleaned neem leaves along with cotton with a liter of water for approx. 10 mins. Cool. Use as an eyewash in case of conjunctivitis, itching etc.

❑ For athlete's foot and other foot problems, make a strong tea and soak feet.

❑ For dandruff and head lice, massage neem oil mixed with coconut or olive oil into hair and leave for 1 hour. Shampoo. Repeat once weekly for 3 weeks or as long as problem persists.

❑ To treat a sore throat without antibiotics, gargle with

neem leaf water (add 2 - 3 neem leaves to 300 ml water and cool) to which honey has been added.

❏ For acne, pimples and skin infections, pure neem leaf powder mixed with water to the affected area.

❏ In case of sinusitis, use pure neem oil as nasal drops. Two drops each in the morning and evening.

❏ Prevent breeding of mosquitoes by adding crushed neem seeds and neem oil to all breeding areas. Neem products ensure complete inhibition of egg laying for seven days.

❏ Add 30 ml of neem oil to 1 ltr of water. Mix well. Add 1 ml of teepol (liquid detergent) and spray immediately for plant protection. Do not store the mixture; make fresh formulation for each spray.

❏ Boil 40-50 neem leaves in 250 ml of water 20 minutes. Cool, strain and refrigerate to use as a astringent.

❏ Chewing 2-3 neem leaves regularly helps purify the blood and in cases of hyperacidity and diabetes.

❏ To ward of mosquitoes, add 5-10% neem oil to any oil and light as a diya (lamp).

❏ Add shake dried neem leaves for preservation of food grains like rice, wheat, lentils etc. The leaves should be replaced every 2-3 months.

Store neem oil in a cool dark place, away from sunlight. In case neem oil solidifies due to low temperatures, put the bottle in warm water (below 95 degree F) to liquefy. Putting the bottle in very hot water may reduce the effectiveness of oil.

❏❏

SPECIFIC BENEFITS OF NEEM

Neem is regarded as a powerful supporter of the body's natural defence mechanisms. Thus it helps support natural immunity, and helps protect the body from free radical damage. Free radicals have been implicated in a number of diseases as well as premature aging.

Because it offers the bitter and astringent tastes, neem is especially helpful for balancing *pitta* and *kapha* doshas.

Neem leaves are regarded by Ayurvedic healers as an effective internal cleanser. Neem leaves have a powerful purifying effect on the blood and help cleanse the liver and skin of toxins. Neem leaf tea with a dash of honey can help soothe a dry irritated throat.

Neem bark is cooling and astringent, and is particularly helpful when taken internally for *pitta*-related issues such as excess stomach acid and premature thinning and graying of the hair. It is also helpful in alleviating tiredness and helps maintain oral health, including healthy gums. Externally, neem bark has been used for centuries by people in India to clean the teeth and gums. It helps maintain oral health and purifies the breath because of its anti-bacterial property.

Neem's anti-bacterial and anti-fungal properties have been well known for centuries and find extensive application today in soaps, shampoos and other skin formulations.

Neem is regarded as a *twacha rasayana* in the Ayurvedic literature—an herb that is excellent for the skin. Neem has a purifying and clarifying effect, drawing out excess oil and smoothing out blemishes, so it's wonderful for persons with *kapha* (earth or water predominant) skin. It is also soothing for dry, irritated skin when combined with Aloe Vera or rose water. Because its cooling nature, neem is also helpful for *pitta*-related skin inflammation.

Neem also helps maintain healthy nails. Neem oil can help restore damaged cuticles or brittle or yellowed nails with regular use. Taking neem internally also helps keep skin, hair and nails healthy. In addition to maintaining the colour and strength of hair, Neem can also help with a dry, flaky scalp and lice. Mix a few drops of pure neem oil with a base oil such as coconut for pitta and sesame for kapha and apply comfortably warm oil to the scalp, covering the hair strands as well. Wrap your hair in a warm towel and leave on overnight or for as long as you can before you shampoo.

Neem is also regarded as *chakshushya*—an herb that is good for the eyes.

With so many therapeutic applications, little wonder that neem has been called 'the village pharmacy' in India and is gaining increasing attention from researchers all over the world.

□□

NEEM PRODUCTS

Neem and its parts are available in powdered form which are put to many uses in industries ranging from cosmetics to oral care, from agriculture to medicine.

NEEM POWDER

Neem powder is used in agriculture to protect plants from insects and pest, it can also be applied as an organic manure. It is also used in veterinary medicine to cure worms, intestinal problems and other internal as well as external infections.

Neem Powder used in Different Products

- Facial creams
- Medicated creams
- Capsules
- Pesticides and insectides
- Veterinary Products
- Personal hygiene products like soap and tooth powder
- Incense sticks
- Coils

NEEM SKIN PRODUCTS

Neem tree has since long been used to treat various skin ailments like acne, blemishes, pimples ete. Traditional medicine systems like ayurveda and unani have been using neem and its parts to cure different skin problems. In the current scenario, neem and its parts are being extensively used in raw form and as extracts to manufacture quality

skin care products; they are exported to countries like US, UK, Australia. Though initially India, Burma and other countries were using neem on a large scale to manufacture natural or herbal goods, but of late, countries like Brazil are also cultivating the magical tree on a large scale to use them in skin care products. A small patch test is generally recommended by manufacturers, as the active ingredients in the products might react; neem products however have no side effects and are safe to use.

Part of Neem Used for Manufacturing Skin Products

Neem Leaf Extracts : These concentrated extracts have rejuvenating and detoxifying effects on the skin; leaf extracts help to purify the skin, remove blemishes and prevent pimples and acne.

Neem Oil : is being used to manufacture moisturizing lotions, skin creams, medicated acne creams and lotions. Topical application is extremely effective in treating almost all skin related problems; it moisturizes and smoothens the skin.

NEEM SPRAY

Neem spray are gaining popularity for being used in agriculture and farming. It is also used for animal health and as a pest repellent. It is more popular because of its organic nature and having no negative effects.

Types of Neem Spray

Spray for Pets : Reduces the chance of skin infections in pets and keeps them free form fleas and ticks. Contains no pyrethrins or synthetic chemicals.

Pesticides and Insecticide Spray : A must have for every farmer and gardener, neem seed oil helps to protect the plants from pests and insects like aphids, white flies, beetles etc.

NEEM OIL

Neem tree is being grown on a commercial basis in US and other countries such as India, Burma and Australia for use in various industries like agriculture and cosmetic etc. Neem oil and its extracts are one of the most useful by products of the magical tree. Neem seed oil is the most effective and is widely used for a large number of applications.

Neem Oil Processing

Mechanical Press Method : This method is one of the oldest methods of processing oil. Seeds are placed in a tub or container and a form of press or screw is used to squeeze the seeds until the oil is pressed out and collected.

Steam and High Pressure Method : This method makes use of high pressure extraction method to squeeze out oil from seeds. Seeds are heated in steam and under high pressure enabling maximum extraction of oil. This method is not very good as most of the active ingredients and compounds are destroyed by high temperature.

Solvent Extraction Method : One of the most used methods of extracting neem oil, it uses a solvent, preferably an petroleum solvent/alcohol solvent for processing oil. It ensures maximum extraction of oil.

Cold Pressed Method : This method of extracting oil is

the most used by leading manufacturers though it is more expensive than the other methods.

Uses of Neem Oil in Various Industries

Cosmetic Industry : Neem bark, seed and leaf oil is being increasingly used in manufacturing a large number of skin products, body lotions, beauty care facial packs in combination with other natural ingredients. The herbal cosmetic industry is in the boom stage, this is an open invitation for the neem oil manufacturers to produce high quality neem oil for use in the cosmetic industry, all around the globe.

Agricultural Industry : The principle ingredient in Azadirachtin found naturally in neem seed oil is being used the world over for manufacturing:

☐ Natural Pesticide

☐ Natural Insecticide

☐ Natural Fungicide

Herbal Medicine Industry : Neem seed, leaf and bark oil is used to manufacture herbal medicines. It can be used as raw neem oil, oil extract to be used in wide medicinal applications.

NEEM TEA

Neem leaf tea is a herbal tea, possessing various medicinal and curative properties. It is being cultivated and grown in a number of countries. Natural neem tea bags are also increasingly becoming popular.

The growing popularity of neem tea has been because of the shiting consumer loyalty from synthetic to 100% natural or herbal products. Manufacturers are producing large scale quantities of neem tea as it does not contain caffeine and is targeted to health conscious people. This specialised tea also has anti bacterial property meant for cleansing the body.

Use of Neem Tea

☐ This natural/herbal tea not only offers refreshment but also include blends of other herbs and are designed to fight diseases like common cold, cough, congestion, digestion problems etc.

☐ Helps to clean the system and increase the immunity.

☐ Good blood purifying agent.

NEEM GEL

Neem and all its parts like seeds, leaves, bark, roots, fruits are being used to manufacture natural gel products, which are further put to many uses.

Kinds of Neem Gel

Neem Hair Gel : It is used as a hair conditioner and promoting hair growth, keeping the scalp clean and free from dandruff.

Neem Face Gel : The anti bacterial, anti fungal properties of neem is used to manufacture medicated and non medicated facial gels to keep the skin smooth, soft and free from acne and pimples.

Neem Tooth Gel : The anti bacterial property of neem is used to manufacture neem gel which maintains the oral hygiene and helps prevent periodontal diseases.

Neem Antiseptic Gel : Can be used for cuts, abrasions, burns, wounds and corns.

NEEM HAIR PRODUCTS

Owing to the popularity of neem tree all across the globe, there has been a significant surge in the demand for neem hair products in the personal hygiene industry. This coupled with the fact that neem products do not have any side effects has made it more popular. Markets in a number of Asian countries and the western world are flooded with hair care products having neem either in the raw form, extracts or as powder. It is either the main ingredient or is mixed with other popular plants like shikakai, amla for healthy hair care and maintenance. Neem is used to manufacture a number of hair products like

❑ Neem Shampoo

❑ Neem Hair Oil

❑ Neem Hair Conditioners

❑ Neem Hair Rejuvenating Tonics

Neem oil, neem leaves are an active ingredient in a number of herbal hair care products. Powdered neem seeds are used in a number of anti dandruff shampoos as it is very effective for curing the problem.

Since neem is found naturally, so the products from it do not have any side effects. With the growing awareness in the effectiveness of herbs, manufacturers are using neem in a host of products. Neem leaves is said to be an effective cure for falling hair and preventing hair loss; thus it is also used in a number of hair fall control lotions.

Neem is also used as capsules, taken orally to prevent hair fall and dandruff.

NEEM SOAP

Neem finds Neem tree and its derivatives are used to manufacture neem based soaps. Neem has antibacterial, antifungal, antiviral properties which helps to keep the skin soft and supple, helps to protect the skin from eczema, infections, acne and nourishes it. Neem soap is also

recommended by doctors to prevent and treat acne. These soap bars are vegetable based and contain pure essential oils to rejuvenate and soothens the skin. Neem soaps are beneficial for super sensitive skins. These premium 100% natural soaps are animal fat free and do not make use of any chemical compounds or artificial fragrances. Leading FMCG companies are venturing into and coming out with neem soaps to cater to the ever increasing demand of neem based soap.

NEEM REPELLENT

Neem is used as an active ingredient for manufacturing insect/mosquito repellent spray and coil. This natural or herbal product is increasingly becoming popular as the fumes are non toxic and do not affect humans. Synthetic repellents and sprays affected the human body, so they are being replaced by the organic counterparts. Repellent creams are being exported to large number of countries infested with insects and mosquitoes.

Azadirachtin is the main compound possessing repellent properties and hence finds immense importance in agriculture and personal hygiene industry. Salannin is another compound in the tree, having insect and pest repellent properties.

Parts of Neem used for Manufacturing Repellent Neem oil : The scent of neem oil prevents the insects from biting, thus acting as a herbal and safe repellent.

Neem leaf extracts : have been successfully used to manufacture herbal and natural repellent creams and coils.

NEEM CANDLE

Traditionally neem candles performed the dual purpose of providing light and repelling the insects. Neem candles have gained popularity because not only do they repel insects but its fragrance soothes the mind and body. Neem parts being used to manufacture bio degradable aromatherapy candles. Neem cake is used to manufacture candles.

As the candle burns, it emits soothing vapors, calming the mind and body, rejuvenates and refreshes the mind.

❒ Benefits of Neem Candles

❒ Used in aromatherapy

❒ Eco friendly and bio degradable

❒ Non toxic

❒ Insect repellent

❒ Neem Incense Sticks

Neem is also being used to manufacture herbal and natural incense sticks. Fragrances have known to refresh the human mind, body and soul. According to number of researches conducted, it can help achieve mental clarity, soothe the nerves, and sharpen senses. Neem incense sticks are gaining popularity because of the fact that they not only provide fragrance but at the same time is useful to drive away insects and mosquitoes.

Another factor which contributes to their success is the fact that these sticks are not toxic and do not emit any harmful fumes. They can be used for both indoor as well as outdoor purpose. Manufacturers and exporters are coming out with numerous blends of natural fragrances to produce high quality incense sticks as there is a growing market for these products especially in countries like US, UK and Australia.

Advantages of Neem Incense Sticks

❐ Can be used along with other natural fragrances to soothe the mind widely used in aromatherapy.

❐ Can be used to drive away mosquitoes, without harming the people around.

❐ No danger of toxic or harmful emission of fumes.

❐❐

ADDITIONAL USES OF NEEM

The neem tree may be used to line avenues, to border roads or fields and in mixed cultivation with fruit trees. The average annual fruit yield from a mature neem tree is above 20 kg. Apart from insecticides, neem oil may be extracted from the seed. 30 kg neem seeds produce 6 - 8 kg oil. The resulting residue can be used to make insecticides in a similar way as from the whole neem seeds described earlier.

All parts of the neem tree can be utilized. Insecticidal substances are present in various parts of the tree; the highest concentrations are, however, contained in the seeds.

Azadirachtin, the most important insecticidal substance contained the plant, has, even in very small doses, a growth disrupting effect on many insect larvae, i.e. insects which eat this substance are unable to develop to the next larval / nymphal stage and die off. Other pests, such as grasshoppers, avoid or reduce feeding as a reaction to azadirachtin. As tests have repeatedly confirmed, due to its special mode of action, the neem extract is quite harmless for useful insects. Unlike synthetic pesticides, tests carried out over a longer period indicate that development of any resistance to the neem extract is in the short term unprobable. However, where intensive vegetable cultivation is practiced, the exclusive use of neem extract is inadvisable.

One great advantage of the neem extract is that even after repeated application on vegetable crops, it remains perfectly harmless for humans.

Home remedies with Neem

☐ Apply Crushed fresh leaves of neem on acne. In case of body acne mix fine paste of fresh neem leaves in little water and smear this mixture on back, chest and shoulders.

☐ In itching, application of neem oil on affected areas helps. Boil neem leaves in a big bowl of water and mix this in bathing water. This reduces body itch.

☐ Massaging neem oil to scalp removes head lice and prevents formation of dandruff.

☐ Mix dry neem powder, shikakai and amla in water and apply this as pack on head. This pack has to be kept for 45 minutes and washed off later. This prevents hair-loss and dandruff. Fresh neem leaves can also be used instead of dry Neem powder.

☐ A freshly prepared paste of turmeric, neem and sesame seeds is recommended in Ayurveda for fungal infection between toes.

☐ Fumigating the house with smoke of dried neem leaves in evenings for 1-2 minutes is an excellent Ayurvedic method to keep mosquitoes away.

☐☐

ECONOMIC POTENTIAL & INDUSTRIAL USES

Neem bark contains tannins which are used in tanning, dyeing, etc. Compounds extracted from neem bark are used in production of some dental-care products. Neem bark is also tapped for gum. Neem seed pulp is useful for methane gas production. It is also useful as carbohydrate—rich base for other industrial fermentations.

Economic Benefits of Neem Production

Neem tree has great potential to help small and marginal farmers in rural India, Africa and Latin America. Farmers, who have limited resources, can benefit in many ways from neem. There are easily exploitable, employment and income generation opportunities in the cultivation of neem and processing of neem products, some of which are possible in a decentralized manner on the basis of small investments.

Economic Potential of Neem in the Future

According to some estimates, there are about 20 million neem trees in India. A neem tree normally starts fruiting after 3-5 years. In about 10 years it becomes fully productive. Under favourable conditions fresh fruit yield per fully grown tree is about 50 kg per year. If 50% are accessible and tapped, the total neem seed production may well reach the level of 5 million quintals. Present level of collection is far below 50% which shows the potential for additional employment and income generation. If commercial plantation and agro-forestry involving neem in popularized, the potential goes up significantly, with positive and large externalities for pesticides, fertilizers, livestock, dairying and other value-added products.

Organic Farming & Neem

The neem tree and its derivatives have great relevance in organic farming practices. This remarkable tree has been identified as a renewable resource for home grown agro-chemicals and nutrients which are bio-degradable, non-toxic and effective.

Pest Management

Neem seeds and leaves contain many compounds which are useful for pest control. Unlike chemical insecticides, neem compounds work on the insect's hormonal system, not on the digestive or nervous system and therefore does not lead to development of resistance in future generations. These compounds belong to a general class of natural products called 'limonoids'.

Fertilizer Uses

Indian farmers have traditionally used deoiled neem cake as a fertilizer in their fields. The dual activity of neem cake as fertilizer and pest repellent, has made it a favoured input. Neem leaves have also been used to enrich the soil. Together, they are widely used in India to fertilize cash crops. When neem cake is ploughed into the soil it also protects plant roots from nematodes and white ants. Farmers in southern parts of India puddle neem leaves into flooded rice fields before the rice seedlings are transplanted.

□□

NEEM FRUIT COLLECTION AND DEPULPING

The collection and depulping of neem fruit is done both manually and machnically. It is not an easy process.

Neem Fruit Collection

The neem yields fruits during May to August every year. The ripend fruits to be collected for the processing. Cover the ground below neem tree with cotton or jute cloth, or shade net to avoid contact of neem fruits with soil. It will also facilitate the collection of the fruits. Being rich in carbohydreates neem fruits gets attacked by fungi, when came in contact with soil. Such fruits may get infected with toxin developing fungus and may damage the quality of the final products prepared from these fruits. Hence it is strongly recommended to avoid contact of neem fruits with soil. As the fruit ripes during rainy season they must depulped as early as possible. Avoid storage of fresh, wet fruits in the plastic bags. Use bamboo baskets or jute bags for storage.

Depulping of Neem Fruits

Depulping is a process to remove seed coat and pulp from the neem seed. It is done by hand and using mechanical depulper. Rub the ripe neem fruits between palms in the bucket of water and wash the seed. Use clean water for depulping. Neem Research and Technology Development Centre (NRTDC) developed a mechnical depulper to handle large quantity of neem fruits. After depulping and cleaning dry the neem seed in the shade in a thin layer. Select the place with good airation. Do not make heap of the seed. Protect it from direct rains. After drying neem seed upto 11% moisture store it in a jute gunny bags or bamboo baskets. Do not store in plastic bags as it may damage the quality of seed. Keep the neem seed in a cool and dry place. If processed properly these neem seeds can be stroed for 6-12 months. It is recommended to use neem seed for prepration of extract or oil extraction after 3 months and before 8 months. The highest concentration of limnoids and oil found after 3 month and before 8 months period.

Neem Kernel Aqueous Extract

The simple method of Neem Kernel Aqueous Extract prepration consist of following steps -

Take dried neem seed. Decorticate (Removal of seed coat) it with the help of mortar and pastle or any mechanical decorticator. Clean the neem kernel and seed coat mixture by winnowing seed coat.

Weigh 1 kg of clean neem kernel and make powder of grain size like fine tea powder. It should be pounded in such a way that no oil comes out. Soak it in a about 10 litres of clean water. Add 10 ml of pH neutal adjuvant (mixture of emulsifier, spreader etc.) and stir the mixture. Keep the mixture overnight and filter it on the next day with clean muslin cloth. Put water in the residue and repeat the extraction 2-3 times. Use residue as a manure for plants.

Spraying of NKAE

The spraying of 1.25% to 5% (Neem Kernel wt. Basis) of NKAE is recommended on the crops. The use of is recommended as a preventive at lower concentration and protective at higher concentration *i.e.* upto 5 %. Use the spray solution on the same day. Spraying should be done in the low intensity of sunlight preferablery in the afternoon. The effect of the NKAE remains for 7-10 days. Care to be taken to cover all plant foliage with NKAE.

Neem Leaf Extract

For 5 litres of water, 1 kg of green neem leaf is required. Since the quantity of leaves required for preparation of this extract is quite high (nearly 80 kg are required for 1 hectare) this can be used for nursery and kitchen gardens. The leaves are soaked overnight in water. The next day the leaves are grounds and the extract is filtered. The extract is beneficial against leaf eating caterpillars, grubs, locusts and grasshoppers. To the extract, emulsifier is added as mentioned in kernel extract.

Neem Cake Extract

100 gms of neem cake is required for 1 litre of water. The neem cake is put in a muslin pouch and soaked in water. It is soaked overnight before use in the morning. It is then filtered and emulsifier is added 1 ml for 1 litre of water. It can then be used for spraying.

Neem Oil Spray

15-30 ml neem oil is added to 1 litre of water and stirred well. To this emulsifier is added (1ml/1litre). It is very essential to add the emulsifier and mix properly. This should be used immediately before the oil droplets start floating. A knapsack sprayer is better for neem oil spraying in preference to a hand sprayer.

Precautions for using Neem Extracts/Formulations : Spraying should be undertaken in the morning or late in the afternoon. Insects lay eggs on the underside of the leaves. Hence it is important to spray on the underside of the leaves as well.

Caution

The active principles of neem are destroyed by :

☐ Heating and boiling the extract—do not boil the mixture.

☐ Acidic or alkaline pH emulsifier—use neutral pH emulsifier.

☐ Ultraviolets rays of sunlight—spray during moderate sunlight.

☐ Hydrolysis of water—use aqueous extract on same day.

☐☐

FOR PROTECTING STORED GRAINS

One of the traditional uses of neem in Asia has been for controlling pests of stored products. Farmers usually mix neem leaves with grain before keeping it in storage for several months. Neem leaves, oil or extracts acts as repellent against several insects such as weevils, flour beetles, bean-seed beetles and potato moths. Treatment of jute sack by neem oil prevents the penetration of pest like weevils and flour beetles. Neem oil destroys bean-seed beetles at the egg-stage itself. A mixture of neem leaves with clay and cow-dung develops pest resistant property so it can be used to make bins for storage of grain.

Post-harvest losses are notoriously high in developing countries. Worldwide annual losses in store reach up to 10% of all stored grain, *i.e.* 13 million tons of grain lost due to insects or 100 million tons to failure to store properly.

While neem treatments cannot replace completely chemical pesticides used in stored products preservation, the amounts of pesticides needed could be reduced, thereby decreasing the pesticide load in food grains. With proper timing and innovative methods of application, their use could be integrated in stored products management.

□□

NEEM AND ENVIRONMENT

In Indian culture neem has been referred to as an air purifier and has been traditionally planted either in the backyard or beside the house. Recent scientific studies have indicated that the Neem tree has the capacity to absorb environmental pollutants and act as an air freshener by releasing oxygen and mild odourous principles. In a study by the scientists of National Environmental Engineering Research Institute, Nagpur, India, it was found that sites with Neem as a dominant species have higher SPI (Sink Potential Index). The data also proved that the Neem tree is one of the most suitable species for checking urban pollution in the industrial locations and it has potential in green belt development in hot spots with known history of high air pollution.

Socio-economic benefits of Neem

Neem plantation provides income by collection of neem fruits in rural areas as demand of neem fruits is increasing day by day. Neem can save crop protection expenses to large extent thus may help to increase profit in agriculture. Neem processing technologies like prepration of neem seed powder, neem aqueous extracts, neem oil and neem cake will create large employment in the rural areas. Use of neem in agriculture can reduce the load of poisonous chemicals in the environment as toxication by these pesticides may cause serious health hazards having impact on the working efficiency and financial condition of the farmers.

□□

NEEM AS ANIMAL FEED

Neem leaves contain appreciable amount of protein, minerals and carotene and adequate amount of trace minerals except zinc. These may be helpful in alleviating the copper deficiency when feeding straw and dry fodder.

Goat & Camel : Goat and Camel relish lopped neem leaves and quite often these are fed as sole feed to them in winter season when tree is not needed for shed. However, systematic studies are not available on neem feeding by these animals. Keeping in view these animals have the capability to thrive in hot and dry areas, there is considerable scope of rearing them on neem leaves.

Cattle and buffaloes : The Neem leaves have appreciable quantity of digestable crude protein (DCP) and total digestable nutrients (TDN). Cattle can be fed twigs and leaves in small quantities when mixed with other feeds.

Poultry : Neem oil can be used in poultry rations. The fatty acid composition of oil indicates that it is a rich source of long chain fatty acids. It contains azadirachtin, meliantriol and salannin. Neem oil can be used in poultry rations.

De-Oiled Neem Seed Cake in Animal Feed : This can considerably reduce the shortage of protein supplements in high producing animals. Seeds from neem yield sufficient oil and the residual cake is the major by-product. Neem cake consists of all essential and non-essential amino acids including sulphur containing amino acids but with negligible quantities of valine and trytophan. The cake has high crude protein, ether extract and fibre contents. Neem seed cake is a very good source of animal protein. The keeping quality is good and it is not easily spoiled on storage nor is it attacked by fungi. The processed cake can be employed as a good poultry feed. Since the cake is bitter, it acts as a good appetizer. It is also a wormicide.

The use of Neem in veterinary medicine in India dates back to the times of the epic Mahabharata. According to scholars, two of the five Pandava brothers Nakul and Sahadev, who practiced veterinary medicine, used neem to treat ailing and wounded horses and elephants by applying poultices prepared from neem leaves and Neem oil for healing the wounds etc., during the battle of Mahabharata. Ancient Sanskrit literature indicates neem applications as feed and in a large number of prescriptions and formulations to provide health cover to livestock in various forms. Various neem preparations were standardized in the form of oils, liniments, powders and liquids. Ayurvedic scholars recommend the use of neem oil as antipyretic, sedative, anti-inflammatory, analgestic, antihistaminic, anthelmintic and as an acaricide.

Neem has been traditionally used against various livestock insects such as maggots, hornflies, blow-flies and biting flies. Neem is also useful for controlling some bacteria of veterinary importance and against intestinal worms in animals.

□□

HEALTH BENEFITS WITH HERBAL TIPS

Neem is actually not a herb but it works like a herb. Many health benefits are the properties of ever part of nem.

Constipation

Take 4-5 leaves of neem, fennel one gram, four raisings, rose folower petals and little cinna. Make powder of it. Mix this powder in one cup wather and nuse it through fine cloth. Now drink one spoon twice daily to get rid of consipation.

Grind 8-10 leaves of neem in water. Drink this mixture early morning. Though neem is cold, but it leacts well on bowels. If you wish, you can mix 3-4 black pepper and a little sugar to this mixture.

Nausea & Vomiting

Roast 5-7 small stems of neem leaves in ashes. Then mix one small cardamom. and a little salt and powder it. Now take it with one cup of water. You will certainly get relief.

Dysentery

□ Make decoction of sweet neem bark. Drink it two times a day.

□ Sook neem bark in water for 4-5 hours. Then drink it two times daily.

□ You can use powder of neem bask and drink ½ twice a day with one cup water.

☐ Take 2-5 gm. juice of neem leaves; tice or thrice daily.

Cough and Cold

☐ Bring one long wood piece of neem. Take five gm black pepper, 10 gm. neem leaves and mix well with force in one bowl of mud. Then make small pills (of pea size) of this mixture and day these pills in cool place. Now take 2 pills thrice daily with tulsi tea. You will get relief from cold within 24 hours.

☐ Dip nibolis in neem juice and drink this mixture. This is for cough.

☐ If there is cough with sputum, mix ashes of neem leaves with honey and lick it 2-3 times a day.

High Blood Pressure

☐ Drink juice of 25 leaves of neem,two times a day for a week. Then discontinouse for 2-3 days. Again start taking this juice for a week.

☐ Avoid salty-spicy and fat rich food.

Oozing Blood

☐ Wash the wound with water of neem leaves and bark. Then make a paste of neem bark and apply on wound.

☐ Drink boiled water of neem leaves twice daily.

Insect Bite

You can apply the paste made of neem leaves and bark on bites of honey bee, scorpion and other insects. This water may be mixed with honey, black pepul and sendha salt.

Nose Bleed

☐ Grind neem leaves and ajwain in water and apply on back of ears. This will stop bleeding.

☐ If this happends in summer season, squeeze juice of

neem leaves and drink it. If heat of the body can be lowered, nose bleeding will automatically settle down.

Eyes

❒ For most of the eye problems use neem fruit (niboli) by grinding it and making paste of it and apply in eyes two times a day.

❒ Eyes should be washed by neem water twice daily.

Acidity

❒ Take neem bark powder, saunth and black pepper and mix well. Use 8-10 gms powder twice daily with normal water.

❒ Eat fruit of niboli 8-10 daily. This will clear bowels and problme of acidity will be solved.

Skin Problems

❒ Drink neem leaves juice mixed with sugar. This will certainly control many skin problmes.

❒ Use of neem panchang (neem bark, leaves, flower, fruit, stem in equal quantity) and grind it finely. Then apply this paste a palms and soles. This will help in controlling burning.

❒ For pimples, use neem juice daily, two times.

❒❒❒

Set of Small Size

English
General Books

- ☐ Home Gardening
- ☐ 101 Feng Shui Tips
- ☐ 101 Vastu Tips
- ☐ Dadi Maa's Home Remedies
- ☐ How to Increase Sex Power
- ☐ Pregnancy & Child Care
- ☐ Baby Health & Child Care
- ☐ All About Yoga
- ☐ Diabetes Cause & Cure
- ☐ Hypertension Cause & Cure
- ☐ Shed Your Weight
- ☐ How to Increase Your Height

Set of Small English Joke Books

- ☐ Juicy Joke Book (Surendra Mohan Pathak)
- ☐ Midnight Jokes
- ☐ Party Jokes
- ☐ Naughty Jokes
- ☐ Spicy Jokes
- ☐ Tickling Jokes
- ☐ Superhit Jokes
- ☐ Non-Veg Jokes
- ☐ International Jokes
- ☐ SMS Jokes
- ☐ Internet Jokes

MANOJ PUBLICATIONS
761, Main Road Burari, Delhi-110084.

A Treasure of Stories
Specially for CHILDREN

Big Size Illustrated

- 101 Stories from Panchatantra
- Akbar Birbal Stories
- 101 Stories of Grand Mother
- The Arabian Nights
- Vikram Betal Stories
- 101 Moral Stories of Grandpa
- Aesop's Stories
- Jataka Tales
- Ramayana
- Fair Fair Fairy Tales
- The Best Stories for Children
- Mahabharata
- Selected Stories from The Holy Bible
- Witty Tenali Rama
- World's Most Popular Folk Tales
- Hillariously Funny Mulla Nasruddin
- Humorous Stories of Shekh Chilli
- World Famous Adventure Stories
- Stories of Talisman
- Famous Jungle Stories
- Horror Stories
- Ghost Stories
- Hitopadesh
- Singhasana Battisi
- Kissa Hatimtai
- World Famous Bravery Tales
- Famous Mythological Stories
- Shri Hanuman Leela
- World Famous Bedtime Fairy Tales
- World Famous Golden Fairy Tales
- Stories from Vedas
- Ghost stories of Mumbai
- The Real Life Encounters of Ghosts and Spirits
- 44 Fantasy Stories
- Popular Stories of Shrimad Bhagwat
- Great Stories from Mahabharata
- Shri Krishna Leela

MANOJ PUBLICATIONS
761, Main Road Burari, Delhi-110084.